MOTT'S™

A Is for Apple
and all things that grow!

By Megan E. Bryant and Monique Z. Stephens
Illustrated by Liz Conrad

SCHOLASTIC INC.
New York Toronto London Auckland Sydney
Mexico City New Delhi Hong Kong Buenos Aires

A is for apple and all things that grow.

B is for beans
lined up in a row.

C is for cherries that hang from the trees.

D is for dandelions

that dance on the breeze.

E is for eggplant, the biggest I've seen.

F is for fiddleheads, so curly and green.

G is for
green apples

(apples aren't just red!).

H is for honeydew,

as big as your head!

I is for ivy

that climbs up the wall.

J is for Juneberries,

plump, sweet, and small.

Juneberry
JAM

is for kiwis
with tiny black eyes.

L is for lemons,

a sour surprise.

is for mangoes

made ripe by the sun.

is for oranges

that drip down your chin.

P

is for peaches

with soft, fuzzy skin.

R is for raisins

(they're grapes at the start!).

S is for sunflower, with seeds you can eat.

T is for tomato, a fruit that's not sweet.

U is for ugly fruit—

how wrinkly it looks!

V is for violets

that grow by a brook.

W is for watermelons that cover the ground.

X is for
X-mas melon—

you eat it year round!

Y **is for yams,**
sweet, potato-y roots.

Z is for zucchinis,

squash wearing green suits!

Up in trees, on the vine,
or growing underground,

from apples to zucchinis
ABCs are all around!

A   There are 7,500 different kinds of apples grown in the world. On average, each American eats more than 45 pounds of apples every year!

B   Beans have the most protein of any vegetable. Protein is important for strong bones and muscles.

C   There are two types of cherries: sweet and sour. Sweet cherries are delicious eaten just as they are. Sour cherries are good for using in desserts—especially cherry pie!

D   Some people think dandelions are an annoying weed, but they are actually yummy and good for you, too! You can eat the leaves and flowers in a green salad or make tea from the roots. But make sure the dandelions haven't been treated with pesticides or chemicals.

E   Eggplants can be black, white, purple, or lavender. Some eggplants are even striped!

F   Fiddleheads are the tightly curled leaves of the ostrich fern. Boil them for ten minutes for a quick and delicious vegetable treat.

G   Red apples are very popular, but don't forget about great-tasting green apples like Granny Smiths, or even yellow apples like Golden Delicious. (Yep, apples *really* do have great names like these!)

H   Honeydew melons have very smooth skin and juicy, pale green flesh. Eat chilled slices for a healthy snack or include them in a yummy fruit smoothie!

I   Ivy is a pretty evergreen plant that likes to climb anything it can find—houses, fences, rocks, and even trees! Poison ivy isn't actually a form of ivy at all, but it can cause an itchy red rash—so be careful not to touch it!

J   Juneberries are very similar to blueberries. Some people call them saskatoons!

K   Kiwis taste tangy-sweet and contain lots of vitamin C. They're also quick and easy to eat: slice them in half and scoop out the fruit with a spoon, or eat them whole, skin and all! (Just be sure to rinse and dry well before eating.)

L   Lemons and lemon juice are used in lots of different recipes, including lemonade. Lemons are also used in perfume and even some medicines!

M   Mangoes are the most popular fresh fruit in the entire world.